MOFFITT

A busy day for Okoth

A Busy Day for Okoth

OUR WORLD OF PEOPLE SERIES

Kenya

A Busy Day for Okoth

Library of Congress Catalog Card Number: 67-16756

By Frederick J. Moffitt

Illustrated by Mae Gerhard

CONSULTANTS:

V. PHILLIPS WEAVER, Associate Professor
of Early Childhood—Elementary Education,
Unversity of Maryland

CHRISTINE B. GILBERT, Librarian,
Plandome Road School, Manhasset, New York;
Adjunct Associate Professor of Library Science,
Graduate Library School, Long Island University

DESIGNER: FRANK CRUMP

SILVER BURDETT COMPANY
A Division of General Learning Corporation
Morristown, New Jersey • Park Ridge, Ill. • Palo Alto • Dallas • Atlanta

4

Okoth, He-Who-Was-Born-When-It-Rained,
lives in Kenya. Kenya is part of the great continent
of Africa, where the sun shines very hot.

Kenya is a big country of mountains and
rivers and plains. Sheep and cattle graze
on pastureland. Elephants and lions roam through
fields and brush. Hippos take lazy mudbaths
in rivers and waterholes. Birds with brilliant
feathers sing in treetops.

It is August and the rainy season is over. Early one morning, Okoth climbs a big rock. This is his favorite place to think and dream.

He gives a twisted grin and rubs his aching jaw. Six of his lower front teeth have just been pulled.

When boys of the Luo tribe are about eight years old, before the roots of their second teeth have grown too deep, a member of the tribe performs the tooth-pulling ceremony. It is a simple step, but an important one in growing to be a man.

Okoth remembers what *Baba*, Father, told him, "A man of Africa must learn to be brave and laugh at pain."

6

Okoth thinks about what today will bring and he forgets his pain.

Grandfather is coming for a visit, and for the occasion Baba has promised Okoth that he may choose a lamb at the market place. Usually, only men choose the lambs, so Okoth feels grown-up.

"Okoth!" calls Mama from the house. "We're about to leave."

Okoth is glad that the family is going to market. He waves good-by to Baby Sister Akelo, She-Who-Was-Born-In-The-Afternoon.

Baba leads the way. He carries a heavy club. Mama follows next, walking straight and tall. She balances a basket of vegetables on her head. Okoth walks slowly behind.

The family walks nearly a mile. Other families
are on the way, too. All are carrying things to
sell. Okoth chats with his friend Otieno,
He-Who-Was-Born-At-Night.

"When we get to the market place, you can help
select a lamb for Baba's flock," invites Okoth.

"I'd like that," says Otieno. "And after that,
let's go look for the traveling singer."

Baba hears the boys talking. "Don't forget to
meet us by the pond," he says. "Mama will have the
noon meal ready and she will want you there."

"I'll be there," says Okoth. He and Otieno are
soon in the market crowd.

There is noise and confusion at the
market place. It is filled with many people.

Everything interests Okoth. He sees bright
strips of cloth hanging from tree branches. There
are strings of beads and pottery of many
different colors. He looks longingly at all the
wood carvings—especially the hand-carved masks.
The fried nuts and *sim sim,* spicy grain,
make his mouth water.

Each family picks a place to sell things. Sometimes it becomes too crowded, but Okoth and Otieno don't care. They join the children in the meadow. A group plays "Jumping the Stick."

Okoth smiles at Otieno. The boys cannot join in the games until their jaws are well. They must be careful not to walk too far or exercise too much.

Otieno rubs his face tenderly. He doesn't complain, but Okoth knows his friend's jaw hurts.

"Do you want to watch the boys walk on stilts?" asks Otieno.

"I must look for a lamb before I do anything else," says Okoth. As he and Otieno return to the market, they hear bleating. Soon they come to a sheep pen.

Okoth looks at the lambs. Each one is beautiful. Each one has bright eyes.

Okoth hopes Otieno will help him choose. But Otieno says, "While you look at the lambs, I'm going to search for a hunting bow. I'll see you later."

17

Okoth looks at all the lambs again. He doesn't want to disappoint his father by choosing one that isn't healthy.

A very small lamb rubs against Okoth's leg. It begins to bleat. It is very young and it cannot stand very well. The loud noise of the market place frightens it.

Okoth picks it up and the lamb snuggles against him. Okoth laughs to himself. He came to choose a lamb, and instead the lamb chooses him.

"This is the one I want," he tells the sheep farmer. "If you'll mark it for me, I'll bring my father this afternoon to see it."

19

His choice made, Okoth goes through the
market place to find the traveling singer. He loves
to hear the beat of the goatskin drum.

The singer is dressed like a warrior hunter
and he sings about Kenya's struggle for freedom.

Then he stomps about as he sings of a herd of
elephants that crushed a banana grove into
the ground. The singer waves his arms about as
he tells of two brave warriors who drove
the whole herd away.

Okoth hopes someday he and Otieno will do
something brave, so songs will be sung about them.

The sun is now high in the sky.

Okoth feels like a lion who hasn't eaten for a week. It is time to look for Mama and Baba.

Okoth finds them near the pond. After the meal of *posho*, cornmeal, Mama packs the big basket for the trip home.

"Did you find a good lamb for me to buy?" asks Baba. Father has already bought two fine sheep and he hopes his son found a good animal, too.

Okoth nods. "The lamb I chose is small, but it is plump and clean and it has no ticks. The farmer is holding it for us. Can we go now?"

23

24

Baba and Okoth hurry to the sheep farmer.
Okoth finds the small lamb at once, and Baba looks at
it closely.

"You made a wise choice, Okoth," he says. "This
is a good lamb. But it's still very young and will
need extra care."

"I'll take care of it," says Okoth proudly.

Baba pays money for the sheep, and he and
Okoth join Mama. The family starts for home. Okoth
carries the little lamb on his shoulders.

"For such a little fellow you are heavier than
a baby elephant," he says. He begins to walk slowly.

"Don't fall too far behind," warns Baba.

The sun is no longer high. The grass is dark.
The shadows become longer. Okoth wishes Otieno
were with him. He is far behind his family.

He hears something howl in the distance.
The little lamb shivers and cuddles closer. "I'll
protect you," comforts Okoth. But he shivers, too.

The howl becomes louder. It is the cry of a
hyena!

Okoth wants to run ahead and find Baba,
but the lamb is heavy and if he leaves it alone
the hyena will attack it.

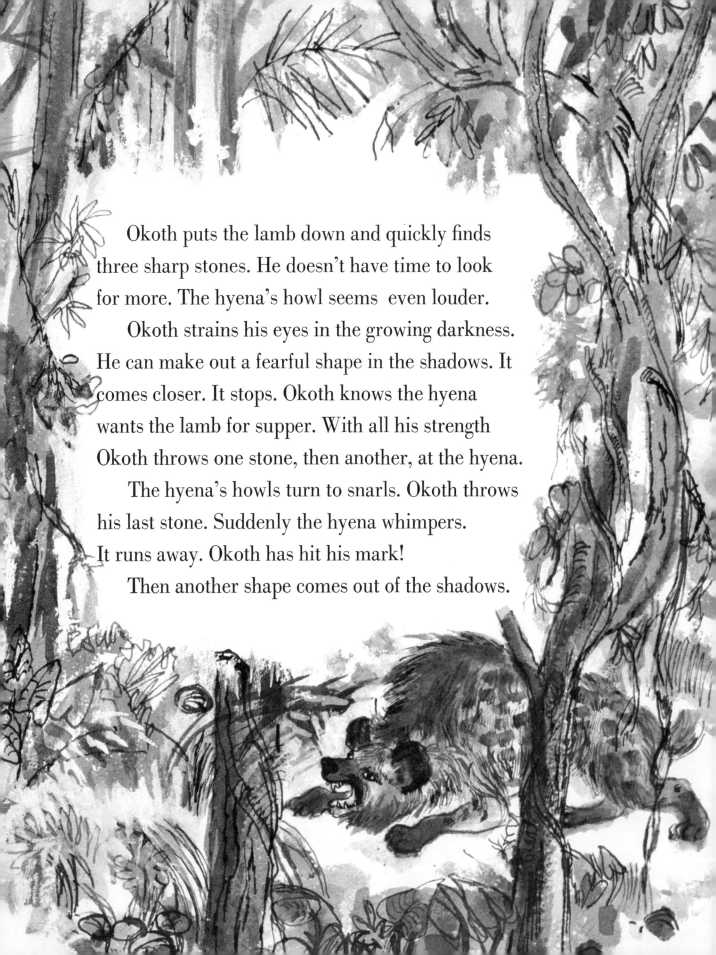

Okoth puts the lamb down and quickly finds
three sharp stones. He doesn't have time to look
for more. The hyena's howl seems even louder.

Okoth strains his eyes in the growing darkness.
He can make out a fearful shape in the shadows. It
comes closer. It stops. Okoth knows the hyena
wants the lamb for supper. With all his strength
Okoth throws one stone, then another, at the hyena.

The hyena's howls turn to snarls. Okoth throws
his last stone. Suddenly the hyena whimpers.
It runs away. Okoth has hit his mark!

Then another shape comes out of the shadows.

It is Baba!

"I heard the hyena and ran back to see if you needed help."

Okoth smiles. "I said I'd take extra care of the little lamb but I didn't think I'd have to fight a hyena for him."

Baba puts an arm around his son. "It is easy to say you will do something. But sometimes it is hard to really do it. Today you kept your word and protected your lamb. I'm proud of you. We will have a good story to tell when Grandfather comes."

30

Helpful Words

Akelo (ah KEE loh), a girl's name

Luo (LOO oh), the name of a tribe in Kenya

Okoth (OH kawt), a boy's name

Otieno (oh tee EN oh), a boy's name

posho (poh shoh), finely ground cornmeal

sim sim (sim sim), grain seasoned with spice, as
   good as candy to Luo boys

32

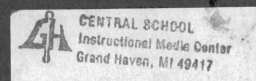